KU-395-807
This
Treasure Cove Story
belongs to
TCS
TCS

JACK-JACK ATTACK

A CENTUM BOOK 978-1-912396-38-2
Published in Great Britain by Centum Books Ltd.
This edition published 2018. 1 3 5 7 9 10 8 6 4 2

Centum Books Ltd, 20 Devon Square, Newton Abbot, Devon, TQ12 2HR, UK.

www.centumbooksltd.co.uk | books@centumbooksltd.co.uk
CENTUM BOOKS Limited Reg.No. 07641486.

Editorial and design assistance: Archibald Reynolds.

A CIP catalogue record for this book is available from the British Library.

Printed in China.

centum

A Treasure Cove Story

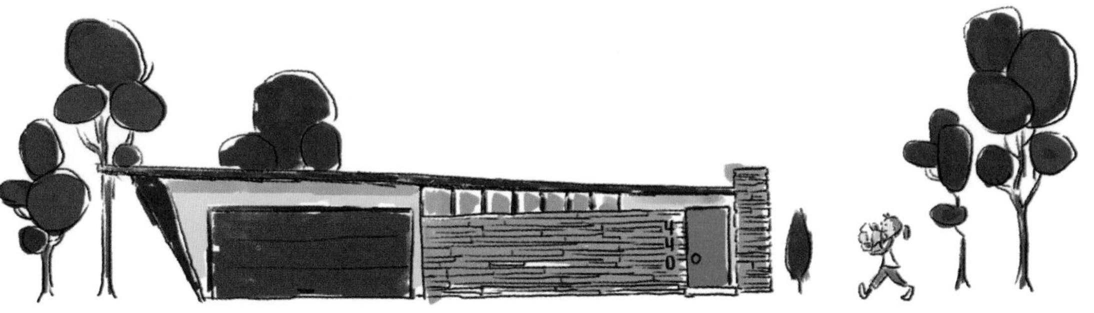

Illustrated by Tony Fucile
Adapted by Mark Andrews and Krista Swager
Based on the short film 'Jack-Jack Attack' written by Brad Bird

Jack-Jack is the baby.

Kari is the babysitter. She comes fully qualified.

It all started out like any normal babysitting job.

What Kari didn't know was that Jack-Jack was not a **normal** baby.

'Who's ready for some neurological stimulation?' Kari cooed to little Jack-Jack.

She arranged some toys on Jack-Jack's play mat and went to put on some music. 'Leading experts say that Mozart makes babies smarter.'

Kari started the music, but when she turned back around, Jack-Jack had vanished. He was suddenly in the dining room.

'Wait… how did you get there?' Kari wondered.

Kari went to the dining room… but Jack-Jack mysteriously appeared in the kitchen!

Kari thought this was all very strange.

'That's weird,' she said. 'Wait right here.'

Kari left a message for Jack-Jack's mum. 'Hello, this is Kari. I have a question about Jack-Jack… Can you call me?'

She turned around…

…and Jack-Jack was gone again!
'Jack-Jack… baby? Where are you?' she said anxiously.

Jack-Jack was sitting on the ceiling.
Splash!
Kari was covered in milk.

Kari thought she had finally found a way to keep Jack-Jack in one place.

Oh, no!

He was up on the bookshelf.

'Be careful, baby!' said Kari.

'You might…

Kari leaped to catch Jack-Jack. She made it just in time…

…to catch his nappy?
Jack-Jack had gone through the floor.

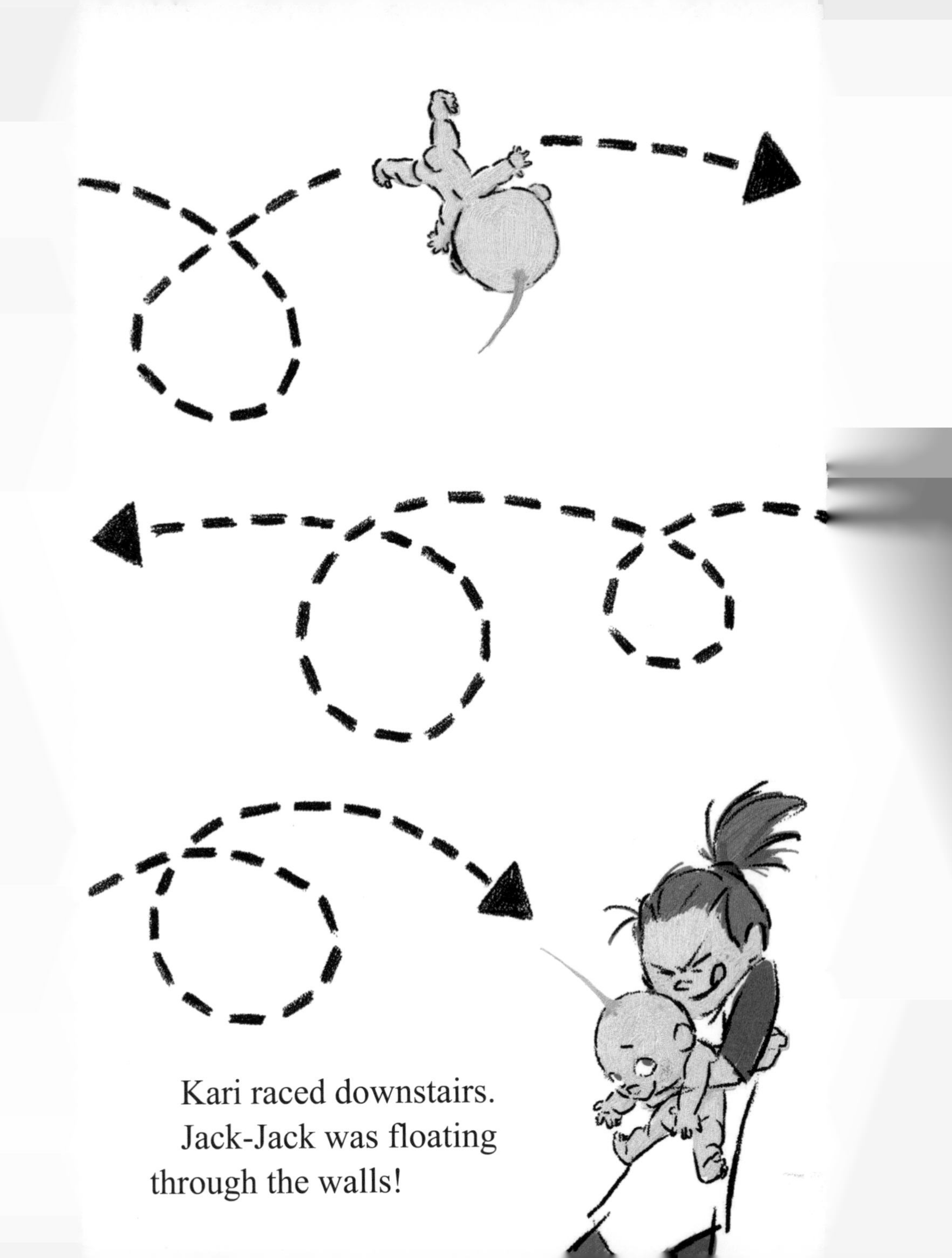

Kari raced downstairs.
Jack-Jack was floating
through the walls!

Kari brought Jack-Jack back upstairs for some quiet time.

'We're gonna look at flash cards,' she said.

A triangle.

A house.

A campfire.

Poof! Jack-Jack burst into flames!
Kari grabbed the fireplace tongs.

She caught Jack-Jack and cooled him off in the bath.

It was a very long night!

But Kari was now prepared for anything. When Jack-Jack burst into flames again, she could manage it.

When he shot burning lasers from his eyes, it didn't surprise her.

After all, she was his babysitter.

Treasure Cove Stories

1 Three Little Pigs
2 Snow White & The Seven Dwarfs
3 The Fox and the Hound - Hide and Seek
4 Dumbo
5 Cinderella
6 Cinderella's Friends
7 Alice In Wonderland
8 Mad Hatter's Tea Party from Alice In Wonderland
9 Mickey Mouse and his Spaceship
10 Peter Pan
11 Pinocchio
12 Mickey Mouse Flies the Christmas Mail
13 Sleeping Beauty and the Good Fairies
14 The Lucky Puppy
15 Chicken Little
16 Mother Goose
17 Coco
18 Winnie-the-Pooh and Tigger
19 The Sword in the Stone
20 Mary Poppins
21 The Jungle Book
22 Aristocats
23 Lady and the Tramp
24 Bambi
25 Bambi - Friends of the Forest
26 Pete's Dragon
27 Beauty & The Beast - The Teapot's Tale
28 Monsters, Inc. - M is for Monster
29 Finding Nemo
30 The Incredibles
31 The Incredibles - Jack-Jack Attack
32 Ratatouille - Your Friend the Rat
33 Wall-E
34 Up
35 Princess and the Frog
36 Toy Story - The Pet Problem
37 Dora the Explorer - Dora and the Unicorn King
38 Dora the Explorer - Grandma's House
39 Spider-Man - Night of the Vulture!
40 Wreck-it Ralph
41 Brave
42 The Invincible Iron Man - Eye of the Dragon
43 SpongeBob SquarePants - Sponge in Space!
44 SpongeBob SquarePants - Where the Pirates Arrrgh!
45 Toy Story - A Roaring Adventure
46 Cars - Deputy Mater Saves the Day!
47 Spider-Man - Trapped By The Green Goblin
48 Big Hero 6
49 Spider-Man - High Voltage!
50 Frozen
51 Cinderella Is My Babysitter
52 Beauty & The Beast - I Am The Beast
53 Blaze and the Monster Machines - Mighty Monster Machines
54 Blaze and the Monster Machines - Dino Parade!
55 Teenage Mutant Ninja Turtles - Follow The Ninja!
56 I Am A Princess
57 Paw Patrol - The Big Book of Paw Patrol
58 Paw Patrol - Adventures with Grandpa
59 Merida Is My Babysitter
60 Trolls
61 Trolls Holiday Special
62 The Secret Life of Pets
63 Zootropolis
64 Ariel Is My Babysitter
65 Inside Out
66 Belle Is My Babysitter
67 The Lion Guard - Eye In The Sky
68 Moana
69 Finding Dory
70 Guardians of the Galaxy
71 Captain America - High-Stakes Heist!
72 Ant-Man
73 The Mighty Avengers
74 The Mighty Avengers - Lights Out!
75 The Incredible Hulk
76 Shimmer & Shine - Wish upon a Sleepover
77 Shimmer & Shine - Backyard Ballet
78 Paw Patrol - All-Star Pups!
79 Teenage Mutant Ninja Turtles - Really Spaced Out!
80 Cars 2 - Travel Buddies
81 Madagascar
82 Jasmine Is My Babysitter
83 How To Train Your Dragon
84 Shrek
85 Puss In Boots
86 Kung Fu Panda
87 Beauty & The Beast - I Am Belle
88 The Lion Guard - The Imaginary Okapi
89 Thor - Thunder Strike
90 Guardians of the Galaxy -Rocket to the Rescue
91 Nella The Princess Knight - Nella and the Dragon
92 Shimmer & Shine - Treasure Twins!
93 Olaf's Frozen Adventure
94 Black Panther
95 Branch's Bunker Birthday
96 Shimmer & Shine - Pet Talent Show

Book list may be subject to change.

An ongoing series to collect and enjoy!

TCS
TCS